printed on
recycled paper